MATH STORIES

$\frac{1}{2}$	FRACTIONS
.5	DECIMALS
%	PERCENTS

JOYCE M. SCINTO

New Readers Press

ISBN 0-88336-748-3

Copyright © 1992
New Readers Press
Publishing Division of Laubach Literacy International
Box 131, Syracuse, New York 13210-0131

Printed in the United States of America

9 8 7 6 5 4 3 2

Table of Contents

FRACTIONS

Adding, subtracting, and multiplying fractions.
Problems are set up in the first five stories.

DECIMALS

Adding, subtracting, multiplying, and dividing decimals.
Problems are set up in the first story only.

PERCENTS

Calculating percentages, using multiplication and division. Problems are set up in the first two stories.

ANSWERS

FRACTIONS

This section includes addition, subtraction, and multiplication of fractions. Problems are set up in the first five stories.

The Butcher

Friday evenings are often the busiest time at the grocery store. Sam works as a butcher at the meat counter and in the deli section.

"What can I get for you this evening, sir? A pork roast? A good choice. Here's one that weighs $7\frac{5}{6}$ pounds. OK? Yes, I'll cut off the pork chops. They weigh $2\frac{1}{6}$ pounds, so you now have a nice-sized roast weighing _____ pounds. Thank you, sir. Have a good weekend."

_____ pounds, roast with chops

\- _____ pounds, pork chops

_____

_____ pounds, roast (reduce)

- -

"Good evening, Mrs. Ikeda. You want to roast a couple of chickens for a special family dinner? How about these two birds? This one is $3\frac{1}{4}$ pounds and this one is $2\frac{3}{4}$ pounds. That's a total of _____ pounds of chicken. Will that be enough? Anything else I can get for you?"

_____ pounds

+ _____ pounds

_____

_____ pounds, 2 chickens (regroup)

- -

"Hi, Mr. Hess. You want meat for sandwiches? How about some boiled ham? Here's $\frac{7}{8}$ pound. The salami is a good deal this week. This much weighs $1\frac{5}{8}$ pounds. The turkey roll is good, too. These three slices come to $\frac{3}{8}$ pound. That makes _____ pounds of meat altogether."

_____ pound, boiled ham

_____ pounds, salami

+ _____ pound, turkey roll

_____

_____ pounds, meat (regroup)

"Evening, ma'am. What can I help you with? This much pastrami? It comes to 1¾ pounds. Should I add a slice or two to make it a round weight of 2 pounds? I'll add _____ pound to make it 2 pounds altogether."

_____ pounds, round weight

− _____ pounds, original weight

_____ pound added

- -

"What can I help you with, sir? You're cooking dinner for your girlfriend and her parents? How about steak? This steak weighs 1⅕ pounds and this one weighs 1⅗ pounds. They ought to be great on the grill. That's _____ pounds of steak altogether."

_____ pounds

+ _____ pounds

_____ pounds, both steaks

- -

"What's on sale this week? The ground beef is a very good buy. This package has 4½ pounds in it. The Italian sausage is on sale, too. How about this package with 1½ pounds in it? The other thing on sale is stew beef. You'd like 2½ pounds? Here you are, ma'am, a total of _____ pounds of meat. Have a good evening."

_____ pounds, ground beef

_____ pounds, sausage

+ _____ pounds, stew beef

_____ pounds, meat (regroup)

- -

When Sam has time, he packages extra ground beef. Right now, he makes packages of 2¼ pounds, 1¼ pounds, and ¾ pound. That's _____ pounds of ground beef.

Friday evenings at work always make Sam tired. But he likes to be busy and he enjoys most of his customers.

_____ pounds

_____ pounds

+ _____ pounds

_____ pounds, ground beef
   (regroup)

Number One

Mr. Morales challenged the students in his night school math class. They had to find two fractions with different denominators that came close to the number one when added together. Mr. Morales said the fractions must add up to less than the number one. The example he gave was $\frac{5}{7} + \frac{3}{14} = \frac{13}{14}$. Here's what the students did.

Carol Hoffman tried $\frac{7}{8} + \frac{1}{16}$. The answer is _____. That's pretty close.

$$\begin{array}{c} \underline{} = \underline{} \text{ (regroup)} \\ + \ \underline{} = \underline{} \\ \overline{} \\ \\ \underline{} \end{array}$$

- -

Peter Krantz handed in $\frac{1}{3} + \frac{5}{9}$. That seems pretty good, too. That equals _____. Several students might be close.

$$\begin{array}{c} \underline{} = \underline{} \text{ (regroup)} \\ + \ \underline{} = \underline{} \\ \overline{} \\ \\ \underline{} \end{array}$$

- -

Cindy Smith added $\frac{3}{4}$ and $\frac{1}{3}$. That comes to (less/more) _____ than one. Mr. Morales (did/did not) _____ accept her problem.

$$\begin{array}{c} \underline{} = \underline{} \text{ (regroup)} \\ + \ \underline{} = \underline{} \\ \overline{} \\ \\ \underline{} \end{array}$$

- -

Cindy's friend, Karen Page, tried $\frac{4}{5} + \frac{2}{15}$. That comes to (less/more) _____ than one. That (was/was not) _____ acceptable to Mr. Morales.

$$\begin{array}{c} \underline{} = \underline{} \text{ (regroup)} \\ + \ \underline{} = \underline{} \\ \overline{} \\ \\ \underline{} \end{array}$$

Billy O'Brien tried the problem $\frac{3}{5} + \frac{3}{10}$, with the answer of _____.

_____ = _____ (regroup)

+ _____ = _____

_____

_____

- -

Red Dean can do numbers with fives and tens best, so he handed in the problem of $\frac{7}{10} + \frac{2}{5}$. That comes to (less/more) _____ than one. Mr. Morales (did/did not) _____ accept Red's answer.

_____ = _____ (regroup)

+ _____ = _____

_____

_____

- -

Jim Norris likes this kind of challenge. He handed in $\frac{5}{8} + \frac{1}{3}$. The answer is _____. That's really close, too.

_____ = _____ (regroup)

+ _____ = _____

_____

_____

- -

Marti Perdue's problem was $\frac{4}{9} + \frac{1}{2}$, which equals _____. Another close one.

_____ = _____ (regroup)

+ _____ = _____

_____

_____

So there were several close answers. Mr. Morales refused a couple of answers because the fractions added up to more than the number one. Who came closest to the number one? The students decided that _____ came the closest.

Union Dues

The union of a large factory sent out a survey to members. The union leaders wanted to set goals for the year. Here's what they found out.

Two-thirds ($\frac{2}{3}$) of the members wanted their wages raised by $1.50 an hour. One-sixth ($\frac{1}{6}$) wanted a raise of $2.25 an hour. Everyone else would go without a raise this year if benefits improved. That _____ (fraction) of the members was more interested in benefits than a raise.

Step one: _____ (fr. = fraction) + _____ (fr.) = _____ (fr.) want raise
               want $1.50   want $2.25

Step two: (1= ___/___) − _____ (fr.) = _____ (fr.) want more benefits
                       want raise

Three-fifths ($\frac{3}{5}$) of the workers wanted Grace Carter as union president. Another $\frac{1}{10}$ of the workers wanted George Mako. The other _____ (fraction) did not have an opinion.

Step one: _____ (fr.) + _____ (fr.) = _____ (fr.) with opinion
          for Grace   for George

Step two: (1= ___/___) − _____ (fr.) = _____ (fr.) no opinion
                    with opinion

One question was about increasing vacation time. There are 260 working days in a year. Workers at the factory get 13 paid vacation days. That is _____ (fraction) of the working year.

$$\frac{\text{vacation days}}{\text{working days}} = \text{_____} = \text{_____ of working year (reduce)}$$

Most of the members, ⅝ of them, wanted dental insurance. One-fourth (¼) of the workers wanted dental insurance and a raise. _____ (fraction) didn't answer the question about dental insurance.

Step one: _____ (fr.) + _____ (fr.) = _____ (fr.) answered question
               dental ins.   ins. and raise

Step two: (1= ___/___) − _____ (fr.) = _____ (fr.) didn't answer question
                       answered

One-third (⅓) of the members wanted a day-care center in the factory. Three-eighths (⅜) said it would cost too much. The other _____ (fraction) had no opinion.

Step one: _____ (fr.) + _____ (fr.) = _____ (fr.) had opinion
           for center   against center

Step two: (1= ___/___) − _____ (fr.) = _____ (fr.) no opinion
                    had opinion

The factory offered a six-week parental leave. One-half (½) of the union members wanted an eight-week leave. One-sixth (⅙) would accept the six-week leave but wanted the same job back. The remaining _____ (reduced fraction) wanted a three-month leave and the same job back.

Step one: _____ (fr.) + _____ (fr.) = _____ (fr.) wanted 6 or 8 weeks (reduce)
         8 weeks   6 weeks

Step two: (1= ___/___) − _____ (fr.) = _____ (fr.) wanted 3 months (reduce)
                  6 or 8 weeks

The union studied the survey results, then set new goals.

Odd Jobs

I saw a TV program the other night about people who do unusual jobs.

Henry Burger trains wild horses. The program showed him training two horses. He said it took him $14\frac{2}{3}$ hours to train Dusty Rose to a saddle. Henry spent $25\frac{5}{6}$ hours training Black Star. That was _____ more hours than Dusty Rose.

_____ Black Star = _____

− _____ Dusty Rose = _____

hours' difference = _____

- -

Studying the weather used to be Mr. Yano's hobby. Now he's the weekend weather reporter for WHOT-TV. He measured $1\frac{1}{8}$" of rain on Saturday night and $1\frac{3}{4}$" on Sunday. He reported a total weekend rainfall of _____ inches.

_____ inches, Sat. = _____

+ _____ inches, Sun. = _____

inches of rain = _____

- -

Ms. Carver is a bee-keeper from California. She keeps her hives in an orange grove. The day of the filming, she sold $15\frac{3}{4}$ pints of orange-blossom honey. The day before, she only sold $11\frac{2}{3}$ pints. The filming brought her luck; she sold _____ pints more on that day.

_____ pints, filming day = _____

− _____ pints, day before = _____

pints more = _____

- -

Connie Jones is a movie make-up artist. She was working on a monster picture. She spent $2\frac{2}{3}$ hours on the first monster, $1\frac{1}{4}$ hours on the second monster, and $1\frac{1}{6}$ hours on the third. Altogether it took Connie _____ hours to make up the three monsters. (Regroup)

_____ hours, #1 = _____

_____ hours, #2 = _____

+ _____ hours, #3 = _____

hours, all three = _____

Freddie Lee is a "roustabout" boss in a circus. He's in charge of tents, animals, and equipment. It takes his crew $6\frac{5}{6}$ hours to set up the tents. Taking the tents down takes them $3\frac{5}{9}$ hours. Wonder why it takes _____ more hours to set them up than to take them down?

_____ hrs., set up = _____

− _____ hrs., take down = _____

_____

hours more = _____

- -

Brian Webb is a sinkhole expert. He examined a new sinkhole that had appeared during the night. It was $10\frac{1}{4}$ feet wide and $5\frac{1}{8}$ feet deep. The next day, it was $17\frac{1}{2}$ feet wide and $10\frac{2}{3}$ feet deep. It had grown _____ feet in width and _____ feet in depth.

Step one:

_____ ft. wide, day 2 = _____

− _____ ft. wide, day 1 = _____

_____

feet wider, day 2 = _____

Step two:

_____ ft. deep, day 2 = _____

− _____ ft. deep, day 1 = _____

_____

feet deeper, day 2 = _____

- -

One day a week, a group of people is paid to laugh at Joey Jerome's jokes during his TV comedy hour. Most weeks, the laughers are there $2\frac{5}{8}$ hours. Once, they had to do half the show over. They were there $3\frac{3}{4}$ hours that day. That was _____ hours longer than usual.

Some jobs really are odd!

_____ hrs., redoing = _____

− _____ usual hrs. = _____

_____

hours longer = _____

Washington, D.C.

Betsy and Ben Williams went on a trip to Washington, D.C. They had always wanted to go there. Thirty-six people went on the three-day trip.

The first afternoon, they went on a bus tour. The tour went to the Washington Monument. It is just over 550 feet tall. Betsy went up 450 feet but got too tired to get to the top. She said her body went up _____ (fraction) of the way, but her heart went all the way.

$$\frac{\text{feet Betsy climbed}}{\text{height of monument}} = \text{_____} = \text{_____} \text{ (reduced fraction)}$$

The tour then went to the Lincoln Memorial. The stop after that was the National Archives. There they saw the Declaration of Independence and the Constitution. They spent 6 hours of the day on the tour, which was _____ (fraction) of the day. (1 day = 24 hours)

$$\frac{\text{hours on tour}}{\text{hours in day}} = \text{_____} = \text{_____} \text{ (reduced fraction)}$$

The next day, they went to the Vietnam War Memorial. Betsy and Ben looked for the names of soldiers they had known. Forty-two people from their area had died in Vietnam. They only had time to find the names of 14. That was _____ (fraction) of those from their area.

$$\frac{\text{names found}}{\text{names looking for}} = \text{_____} = \text{_____} \text{ (reduced fraction)}$$

After lunch, Betsy and Ben went to the Air and Space Museum. They were there from 1:30 p.m. to 4:30 p.m. Ben spent half an hour studying Lindbergh's airplane, the Spirit of St. Louis. Half an hour was _____ (fraction) of Ben's time in the museum. (1 hour = 60 minutes)

Step one:

_____ mins. in hour

x _____ hours in museum

_____

_____ mins. in museum

Step two:

$$\frac{\text{mins. studying plane}}{\text{mins. in museum}} = \text{_____} = \text{_____ (reduced fraction)}$$

The second night, 16 members of the group of 36 went to a concert at the Kennedy Center. The rest went to see the Baltimore Orioles in an exhibition baseball game. That meant _____ (fraction) of the group went to the game.

Step one:

_____ members on tour

− _____ to Kennedy Center

_____

_____ to baseball game

Step two:

$$\frac{\text{to baseball game}}{\text{members on tour}} = \text{_____} = \text{_____ (reduced fraction)}$$

The last day, they went to see Mount Vernon, home of George Washington. Ben was so tired, he sat down and looked at the Potomac River. He figured he had been on his feet for 30 hours in the past 3 days. That was _____ (fraction) of the time. He was ready to go home. (1 day = 24 hours)

Step one:

_____ hours in day

x _____ days

_____

_____ hours in 3 days

Step two:

$$\frac{\text{hours on feet}}{\text{hours in 3 days}} = \text{_____} = \text{_____ (reduced fraction)}$$

Starting a Career

Heidi Duncan has wanted to be a nurse since she was 6 years old. Now she is 18. For _____ (fraction) of her life, Heidi has been dreaming of being a nurse.

First, Heidi had to get a job. She stopped by the neighborhood health clinic. By luck, there was a temporary job open. The regular assistant was going on maternity leave. Heidi got the job. She would get 3 months, _____ (fraction) of a year, of experience.

Twenty-one people work in the clinic on three shifts. Each month they change shifts. Heidi started with the day shift. Her first job was to register 36 pregnant women. The women were coming to Dr. Richards' prenatal class. Twenty of them were expecting to deliver their babies within a month. That was _____ (reduced fraction) of the pregnant women.

Dr. Richards said there were at least 30 other pregnant women in the neighborhood. That was apart from the 36 in the class. Dr. Richards wished she could get all the women to come. About _____ (fraction) of all the pregnant women would be attending the class.

One afternoon, Heidi was at the desk answering the phone. She logged 48 calls in three hours. Six calls, _____ (fraction) of the total, were from women registering for the prenatal class. Eight calls, _____ (fraction) of the total, were about babies or young children. A quarter (¼) of the calls, _____ calls, were about insurance or costs.

People came for regular treatments or medicine in the afternoons. One day, there were 30 people in the waiting room by 2:00 p.m. The clinic van had brought 6 of the patients. So, _____ (fraction) of the patients came by van.

A man came screaming into the clinic. He was carrying a little boy. "He's choking on a cork," yelled the man. Heidi knew what to do. Pop! Out came the cork! Heidi handled the emergency calmly. Nurse Gembler told Heidi that they saw about 150 patients a day. Five or so of the patients had real emergencies. About _____ (reduced fraction) had real emergencies.

Heidi wanted to be a nurse even more than before. She started applying to nursing schools. She got a scholarship at the local nursing school. The tuition was $2,475 per semester. Her scholarship covered $1,650 of that. Heidi had to pay the other _____ (fraction) of the cost.

She went on working at the clinic. The clinic hired Heidi as a part-time nurses' aide. She would be working 14 hours every weekend. She worked 35 hours a week before. Her new hours were _____ (fraction) of her old hours.

Heidi couldn't wait to become a nurse.

Speak Out

A speech class was offered at the community college. The class met on Tuesday and Thursday nights from 7:00 p.m. to 9:00 p.m. Thirty-six people enrolled in the class. Two-thirds (⅔) of the class enrolled in advance. That meant _____ people enrolled before the first class meeting.

The teacher asked the students why they had enrolled. One student had enrolled to meet other people. Two-fifths (⅖) of the rest came to improve their speaking skills for their jobs. So, _____ people took the class for their jobs.

Other students said they hated speaking in front of others. Those students wanted to overcome shyness about speaking. Three-fifths (⅗) of those 35 students were taking the class to learn to speak without being afraid. That was _____ students.

John Ching is Chinese. He wanted to learn to speak English more quickly, the way Americans speak. He spent ¾ hour, 6 days a week, practicing at home. John practiced _____ hours a week.

Brigitte is from Denmark. She wanted to improve her English pronunciation. She used a tape recorder to practice her pronunciation. She practiced 1½ hours every day except Tuesday and Thursday. Brigitte worked on her English with her tape recorder for _____ hours a week.

For the first assignment, each student had to give a talk. Then, other students would comment on the talk. Each student speaker had $\frac{1}{12}$ hour for this first talk. The students each had to talk for _____ minutes.

In this first speech, the students could talk about a special person or an event from their lives. Five-ninths ($\frac{5}{9}$) of the 36 students chose to talk about a person. There were _____ students who decided to talk about an event.

The teacher said that a speaker usually spends $\frac{1}{5}$ of a speech introducing the subject. The speaker also spends $\frac{1}{5}$ of a speech summing up. The rest of the speech should be about the main idea. In a 10-minute speech, a speaker should spend _____ minutes on the main idea.

The teacher suggested 32 topics for the students to speak about. The topics included jobs, family, favorite activities, and politics. Each student had to prepare 8 talks altogether. They each had to choose _____ (fraction) of the 32 topics.

Twelve students wanted to speak on topics that weren't listed. Those students really wanted to talk about something else. Out of the class of 36, _____ (fraction) chose some of their own topics.

On the final night of the course, each of the 36 students gave a $3\frac{1}{2}$-minute talk. The 2-hour class period (was, was not) _____ long enough for everyone to speak.

None of the students seemed afraid to speak out anymore.

14th-Street Firehouse

Thirty-six fire fighters are assigned to the 14th-Street Firehouse. Fire fighting is a demanding job. Eighteen of the fire fighters work at one time, while the other _____ (fraction) of the force is off duty.

The fire fighters get to know one another very well. They are on duty for 84 hours without a break. They eat and sleep there between calls. Usually about ⅓ of the time is spent eating and sleeping. That leaves _____ hours for answering calls and for other duties.

The fire fighters usually spend about 35 hours out on calls for every 84 hours they are on duty. They spend about _____ (fraction) of every 84 hours out on calls.

The firehouse has an emergency medical team. Calls for the medical team usually last about ⅓ hour. The team's job is to get injured people to the hospital as quickly as possible. The team goes out about a dozen times during each 84-hour period. Team members spend about _____ hours on emergency calls. (One dozen = 12)

During the dry summer, a brushfire started. A team of 18 fire fighters couldn't contain the brushfire. They had to call in the other 18 fire fighters. Twenty fire fighters from another station were called in. Sixteen volunteers also came to help. The original team of 18 was only _____ (fraction) of all the fire fighters and volunteers at the brushfire.

One night, the fire fighters were called to a factory fire. The building was valued at $240,000. The fire fighters managed to save only ¼ of it. The destroyed part of the building was worth $_____. The quarter that was not burned was now unsafe. It had to be demolished.

Fire fighting is a dangerous and skilled job. As a fire fighter, Al Freeman gets paid $30,000 a year. He gets paid ½₁₂ of that per month. He earns $_____ each month.

Fire fighters don't just fight fires. They spend some time raising funds. They also give talks in schools and to clubs. Their talks are about fire safety in the home and on camping trips. Fire fighter Ken Jones visited 5 schools and 2 hiking clubs last month. His talk takes ¾ of an hour. Ken spent _____ hours talking about fire safety last month.

At Thanksgiving and Christmas, the fire fighters collect food and toys. Some of the toys need fixing before they can be given to needy children. Last year, fire fighters Olaf Anderson, Helga Gorman, and Evan Smith repaired 270 toys. They spent about ⅔ of an hour on each toy. They donated _____ hours for toy repair.

Fire or no fire, the 14th-Street Firehouse is a busy place.

The Addition

I'm a building contractor. I did a job recently for some neighbors, the Levins. They needed more space, but they didn't want to move. Besides, buying a new house would cost a lot more than building an addition. The plans were for a new family room, 18½ feet by 20 feet. The Levins were adding _____ square feet to their house.

The Levins hired me to do the job. I subcontracted with a carpenter to make the framework for the room. I paid the carpenter for labor and materials. The carpenter's bill came to $1,854. Four-ninths (⁴⁄₉) of the bill was for labor. The rest, $_____, was the cost of materials.

My partner and I planned to finish the carpentry. Before we could do that, we had to hire an electrician. She wired the addition and rewired the rest of the house. The electrician's bill came to $2,116. She paid her assistant ¼ of that. The rest, which was $_____, went toward her salary and equipment.

The plumber installed a bathroom and baseboard heating. He sent a partial bill of $714 before he finished. The remaining ⅗ of the total was due when the job was done and inspected. That remaining ⅗ came to $_____. The total amount I paid the plumber was $_____.

Each roll of insulation material covers 20 square feet. The three outside walls needed insulation. They're 8 feet high. Two of the walls are 18½ feet long. The other wall is 20 feet long. To insulate the floor, the ceiling, and the three walls, we needed _____ rolls of insulation material.

The Levins wanted to have floor tiles in the addition.
I got 370 square feet of tiles at $2.50 per square foot.
The tiles cost $_____.

The wall without windows has built-in shelves. We used
17 feet of shelving. There are 6 sections of shelves. So, each
section of the shelves is _____ feet long.

The Levins bought some smaller shelves for pictures and
ornaments. Each shelf is 8½ inches high. Altogether, those
shelves are 85 inches high. There are _____ shelves.

The Levins saved money by not moving. They love their
new addition, too. We totaled up the cost of the new room.
The total cost for the project came to $9,975. Materials and
outside labor came to ³⁄₇ of that. Materials and outside labor
cost us a total of $_____. So we made $_____.

It took us a month to complete the Levins' addition.
Working at that rate, we would make $_____
in a year. (1 year = 12 months)

The Home Aide

Mrs. Wagner is a home aide. She works mostly for older people who need help doing errands and chores. She goes to a different home every day of the week.

Mondays:

On Mondays, Mrs. Wagner goes to Mrs. Lorenzo's house. Mrs. Lorenzo has arthritis and needs help with cleaning and yard work. It takes Mrs. Wagner $\frac{3}{4}$ hour to mow the lawn, and $\frac{1}{2}$ an hour to edge and trim. Then she spends about $\frac{5}{6}$ hour working in the vegetable garden.
All that yard work takes her_____ hours and
_____ minutes.

Mrs. Wagner spends the rest of the day cleaning the house. She cleans the house in about 3 hours. She cleans the bathrooms, washes the kitchen floor, vacuums, and dusts. It takes her $1\frac{1}{3}$ hours to do the kitchen. The rest of the house takes _____ hour and _____ minutes.

Tuesdays:

Mrs. Wagner goes to Mr. Strout's apartment on Tuesdays. She spends the morning shopping and doing other errands for Mr. Strout. She does his shopping in about $1\frac{5}{6}$ hours. His other errands take her about $1\frac{3}{4}$ hours. Mrs. Wagner is out for about _____ hours. (Regroup.)

Mrs. Wagner spends Tuesday afternoons cooking and cleaning. She worries that Mr. Strout doesn't eat enough. She always makes some soup and a couple of dishes that will last a few days. She's there for 3 hours in the afternoon. She spends $\frac{3}{5}$ of that time cooking. That leaves _____ hours for cleaning.

Wednesdays:

The Medinas only need Mrs. Wagner to come to their house in the morning. They need help with repair jobs. Right now, the window sills and frames need painting. This week, Mrs. Wagner spent $2\frac{5}{6}$ hours removing old paint from the three front windows. The painting took $1\frac{1}{3}$ hours. She worked for _____ hours and _____ minutes. Next week, she'll start on the side windows. (Regroup.)

Some Wednesday afternoons, Mrs. Wagner treats herself to a trip to the mall. She eats lunch and shops for $2\frac{3}{4}$ hours. Then she goes to a movie, usually for about $1\frac{5}{6}$ hours. She gets to the mall at 1:30 and is usually ready to leave by (5:05 / 5:55 / 6:05) _____. (Regroup.)

Thursdays:

Ms. Rio has bad eyesight. She has Mrs. Wagner read to her if there's time. Mrs. Wagner arrives at 11:00 a.m. and cleans for $1\frac{1}{3}$ hours. Then she and Ms. Rio eat lunch together for $\frac{3}{4}$ hour. Ms. Rio takes a nap after lunch for $\frac{2}{3}$ hour. Then Mrs. Wagner reads to her for _____ minutes, until leaving at 2:30 p.m.

Fridays:

Mrs. Wagner works at a retirement home on Fridays. It's rather far from her house. The bus ride from her house is $7\frac{1}{8}$ miles. Then she has to walk for $\frac{3}{4}$ mile to get to the retirement home. She travels _____ miles every Friday to get to the retirement home and back again.

By the time she gets home, Mrs. Wagner wishes she had a home aide for herself.

DECIMALS

In this section you will add, subtract, multiply, and divide decimals. Problems are set up in the first story only.

Olympic Meet

There's plenty of news from the coaches' club this month. Coach Fuller's runner Sean Mitchell won the men's 100-meter dash in 12.01 seconds. A teammate, Arne Borne, came in second at 12.33. Mitchell beat Borne by _____ seconds.

```
_____   Borne's time
-
_____   Mitchell's time
_____
_____   seconds faster
```

In the women's 100-meter dash, Coach Sheridan's candidate, Pat Holland, won in 13.02 seconds. Her nearest competitor had a time of 13.55 seconds. That was _____ seconds slower than Holland's time.

```
_____   losing time
-
_____   Holland's time
_____
_____   seconds slower
```

These Olympic hopefuls are good. Here are some facts and figures to compare. In 1984, the U.S. Olympic Team won the 400-meter relay. Sam Graddy ran his 100-meter leg in 10.29 seconds. Ron Brown came in at 9.19 seconds. Calvin Smith ran his leg in 9.41 seconds. Carl Lewis ran the anchor leg in 8.94 seconds. The team's total time was _____ seconds.

```
_____   Graddy's time
_____   Brown's time
_____   Smith's time
+ _____ Lewis's time
_____
_____   team's total time
```

In 1886, Thomas E. Burke won the men's 100-meter dash in 12.00 seconds. Carl Lewis of the U.S. won the 1984 Olympic 100-meter dash in 9.99 seconds. That was _____ seconds faster than Burke's winning time.

_____ Burke's time

− _____ Lewis's time

_____

_____ seconds faster

At the last swim meet, Tom Paine won the men's 100-meter freestyle. His time was 1:02.34 (1 minute, 2 seconds, and 34 hundredths of a second). Lars Gunderson was second with 1:08.94. Paine was _____ seconds faster.

_____ Gunderson's time

− _____ Paine's time

_____

_____ seconds faster

In the women's events, Dinah Burger from Carlotta won the 100-meter freestyle with a time of 1:52.61. Maria Martello from Clearwater was second with 1:59.72. Her time was _____ seconds slower than Burger's winning time.

_____ Martello's time

− _____ Burger's time

_____

_____ seconds slower

Let's compare some Olympic records. In 1984, Tiffany Cohen of the U.S. swam the 400-meter freestyle in 4:07.10. Her time was 1.66 seconds faster than the 1980 winner. The 1980 winning time was _____ minutes, _____ seconds.

_____ Cohen's time

+ _____ seconds faster

_____

_____ 1980 winning time

The 400-meter relay team of Carey, Lundquist, Morales, and Gaines had a total team time of 3:39.30 in the 1984 Olympics. In 1960, the U.S. team time was 4:05.40. The '84 team was _____ seconds faster than the '60 team.

_____ 1960 time

− _____ 1984 time

_____

_____ seconds faster

The Produce Market

"Bess, would you go to the produce market for me today? I don't have time to go."

"I guess I can go, Mom," said Bess. She'd rather be with her friends, but she went to the market anyway.

At the market, Bess picked out nine plum tomatoes that weighed 2.5 pounds in all. The cost was 49¢ a pound, which is almost 50¢. Bess figured in her head that 50¢ times 2 pounds is $_____. One half of 50¢ is 25¢, so the total cost of the tomatoes would be about $_____.

Bess sees a friend from school. "Oh, hi, Archie. Do you work here?"

"Yes, every Saturday. I'll help you pick out the best produce. How about these strawberries at $1.19 a pint?"

"My mother wants 2 quarts if they are good. I need 4 pints at about $_____ a pint. That comes to about $_____ altogether." (2 pints = 1 quart)

"I need some bananas, too. I'll take that bunch."

"OK. That's 3.5 pounds."

"At 29¢ a pound or nearly 30¢, 3 pounds is _____¢. One half of 30¢ is _____¢. I'll pay about $_____."

Next on the list was a pound of eating apples. Bess picked four apples weighing 1.1 pounds altogether. They were 69¢ a pound, which is about _____¢ a pound. The eating apples cost about _____¢.

"I'll take these 10 baking apples, too. They're 59¢ a pound, which is nearly _____¢ a pound."

"You've got 3.25 pounds of apples here, Bess. That's enough for a pie and some left over. OK?"

"That's fine, Archie. Three times _____¢ a pound is $_____. One quarter of 60¢ is _____¢. They will cost about $_____."

"Now, do you have any green beans?"

"Oh, we have some really tender ones. We just got them in this morning. They're 39¢ a pound. Here, taste one."

"They taste good, Archie. I'll take this bag. Let's see, 39¢ is about _____¢. There are 2.9 pounds or almost _____ pounds in the bag. It will cost about $_____."

Bess decided to buy some fresh spinach, too. The spinach cost $1.39 a pound, which is almost $_____ a pound. The bag that Bess picked weighed 1.5 pounds. One half of $1.40 is _____¢, so the bag of spinach cost about $_____.

"My mother needs 2 heads of lettuce. I see they're 49¢ a head. That will cost about $_____. She also wants one bunch of watercress."

"Here's a good bunch of watercress, Bess. It's 1.25 pounds at 99¢ per pound. That will cost almost $_____ for the pound, and a quarter of that is _____¢. So the watercress will cost about $_____. Anything else, Bess?"

"That's all for today, Archie. Thanks for your help."

Mick the Mechanic

You can tell me your car troubles. I'm Mick, the head
mechanic at The Next-Door Garage. It seems like all my
customers do some figuring when it comes to their cars.
I use math myself. Even though the garage is called
The Next-Door Garage, it isn't next door to where I live.
My house is 7.1 miles from the garage. Yesterday, I found
a shortcut that's only 6.3 miles from home. That's
_____ miles shorter.

Most of the time, I use regular gas in my car and get
19.2 miles per gallon. Sometimes, I use gasohol. It's
a blend of gasoline and alcohol. When I use gasohol,
I get 22.1 miles per gallon. I've heard it's better for the
environment. I also get _____ more miles per gallon.

My friend Max drove here from West Virginia for
Thanksgiving. He drove 263.1 miles in 4.5 hours.
His average speed was _____ miles per hour.
(Round off to the nearest tenth.)

The speedometers in some cars register in both kilometers
and miles. Some countries only use kilometers. Drivers
might like to know that 1.61 kilometers equal 1 mile. So
55 miles per hour is _____ kilometers per hour.

Craig Geter drives a truck. He has to enter his odometer
reading in his log every night. He had to find out how many
miles he drove today. Craig subtracted yesterday's reading
of 30,794.8 from today's reading of 31,201.3. He drove
_____ miles today.

Irene Winsky likes to know how far she travels on trips. Her car's odometer read 23,172.3 miles when she left home to go to St. Louis. It read 23,391.4 miles when she arrived there. She had traveled _____ miles. The next time she goes to St. Louis, she'll know just how far away it is.

Tony Cavallo likes to know how far he goes on a gallon of gas. He figures this out when he fills up his tank. He divides the number of miles since his last fill-up by the number of gallons needed to fill his tank. This is his mileage. He needed 5.6 gallons to fill the tank after driving 168 miles. He figured that he went _____ miles on every gallon. At that rate, he will use _____ gallons on the 417-mile trip to his brother's.

Eric Dash and Jen Spence wanted to know whose car got higher mileage. Eric went 572.04 miles and used 25.2 gallons of gas. Jen went 908.85 miles and used 41.5 gallons of gas. (Eric's, Jen's) _____ car got the better mileage.

Some customers keep accounts at The Next-Door Garage. They pay their bills once a month. Irene's car had a tune-up and two new tires last month. Her bill was $183.87. The month before, her bill was $69.46. The month before that, she paid $117.19. Her average bill for the past 3 months was $_____. (Round to nearest cent.)

Don't forget I'm here if you ever have any questions about your car. Just ask for Mick at The Next-Door Garage.

Baseball Scores

Good afternoon, everyone! This is Ken Cooper, bringing you the game over WRAF-Radio. Now, before we say "Batter up!" let's have a little figuring lesson. Every good baseball fan knows how the experts figure baseball statistics. Be an expert.

Winning Average:

At the end of the season, the teams with the highest winning averages win their divisions. To calculate a baseball team's winning average, divide the number of games won by the number of games played. The Bears played 160 games and won 90 games. The team's winning average was _____.
(Round off to the nearest thousandth.)

The Eagles played 150 games and won 70. Their winning average was _____.
(Round off to the nearest thousandth.)

Batting Average:

The most valuable players are those who get the most hits for their team. These players have the highest batting averages. To calculate a player's batting average, divide the player's number of hits by the number of times the player was at bat. In the first five games of the season, Joe was at bat 20 times and got 7 hits. His batting average for those games was _____.

Later in the season, Joe had been up to the plate 578 times and had 143 hits. That's a pretty good record. His batting average for the season was _____.
(Round off to the nearest thousandth.)

Ty Cobb, known as the "Georgia Peach," was a great player. He was up to bat 11,429 times during his baseball career. He had 4,191 hits, so his lifetime average was _____. (Round off to the nearest thousandth.)

Hank Aaron of the Atlanta Braves holds the career home-run record. He was up to bat 12,364 times and got 3,771 hits. His lifetime batting average was _____. (Round off to the nearest thousandth.)

Earned Run Average:

A pitcher's Earned Run Average (ERA) is the average number of runs a pitcher allows per nine innings. The lower the ERA, the better the pitcher. To calculate ERA, divide the number of innings pitched by 9. That tells you the total number of games. Then divide the number of runs allowed by the number of games. In the first half of the season, Evan pitched 60 innings and allowed 15 runs. Evan's ERA was _____. (Round off to the nearest hundredth.)

Later in the season, Evan had pitched 115 innings and allowed 26 runs. His ERA now was _____. (Round off to the nearest hundredth.)

Won-Lost Percentage:

To calculate a pitcher's won-lost percentage, divide the number of games won by the number of games played. Then multiply by 100 to convert that to a percentage. In 1937, Carl Hubbell of the New York Giants pitched 30 games and won 22. His won-lost percentage for that year was _____%. (Round off to the nearest whole number.)

In 1978, Ron Guidry of the New York Yankees pitched 28 games and won 25. His won-lost percentage for the season was _____%. (Round off to the nearest whole number.)

OK, folks. Now you're ready. Batter up!

PERCENTS

In this section, you will be calculating percentages.
Problems are set up in the first two stories.

Family Budget

Glenda and Joe Mason earn $2,500 a month between them. That's after they've paid health insurance and taxes. They divide their earnings carefully. The rent comes to 30% of their earnings. That means they pay $_____ a month in rent.

$ _____ earnings

x _____% for rent
_____

$ _____ a month, rent

- -

The Masons spend 20% of their earnings on regular expenses like groceries. This amounts to $_____ every month.

$ _____ earnings

x _____% for regular expenses
_____

$ _____ a month, regular expenses

- -

Car payments and gas add up to 12% of the Masons' paychecks. Utilities, such as water, electricity, and telephone are 7%. That means the Masons pay $_____ a month for car expenses and utilities.

$ _____ earnings

x _____% for car and utilities
_____

$ _____ a month, car and utilities

- -

The Masons budget 5% of their income for clothing and shoes for themselves and their two children. They set aside $_____ a month for clothing and shoes.

$ _____ earnings

x _____% for clothing and shoes
_____

$ _____ a month, clothing and shoes

The Masons figure doctors' and dentists' bills into the budget. Their medical bills average 6% of their income over the year. So the Masons set aside $_____ a month for that purpose.

$ _____ earnings

x _____% for medical bills

_____

$ _____ a month, medical bills

- -

The Masons average out car and renter's insurance over the year. They put aside 3% of their income each month. When the insurance bills come, the money is saved already. Their insurance costs $_____ a year.

$ _____ earnings per year

x _____% for insurance

_____

$ _____ insurance per year

- -

The Masons set aside 5% for trips and special gifts. They allow 2% of their $2,500 for regular recreation, such as movies and bowling. They also save 10% every month for one-time expenses such as a new washing machine or car repairs. They'll need a new washing machine soon. It will cost $450. It will take the Masons _____ months to save enough money to buy the new machine.

Step one:

$ _____ earnings

x _____% for one-time expenses

_____

$ _____ saved a month

Step two: $_____ ÷ _____ = _____ months to buy machine
             cost of   saved a month
             machine

Mr. Mason got good news. He got a promotion and a 6% raise on his $18,000 salary. Now his yearly salary is $_____.

$ _____ past salary

x _1._____% (100% + raise)

_____

$ _____ new salary

34

Taxes, Taxes, Taxes

George Martin was having breakfast. The doorbell rang. He answered the door and saw a visitor. The visitor said, "I am from the IRS, Mr. Martin. You sent in your income tax form, but you didn't enclose a check. Your income was $87,510. You owe 30% in federal tax." George wrote out a check for $_____.

$ _____ net income

x _____% federal tax

_____

$ _____ owed

- -

The doorbell rang again. "Mr. George Martin?" George nodded. "You bought a washer and dryer last year? The company forgot to charge you the sales tax. The appliances cost $846. The sales tax is 3% for the state and 3% for the county. That will be 6% of $846, which comes to $_____."

$ _____ cost of appliances

x _____% sales tax

_____

$ _____ owed

- -

As George was getting into his car, a man stopped him. "Mr. Martin, you have forgotten to pay your state income tax. Here's my I.D. You owe 5% of your income for last year." George wrote the check for 5% of $87,510. It came to $_____.

$ _____ net income

x _____% state tax

_____

$ _____ owed

- -

A car was waiting for George at his office.

"George Martin, do you own the house at 2500 Apple Tree Lane?"

"Yes, I do. What's the matter?"

"You owe the county property tax. Your house is worth $280,000, and the tax is 0.5%. That will be $_____." George paid again.

$ _____ value of house

x _____% property tax

_____

$ _____ owed

George thought he had better call his bank and check his account. He'd written so many checks this morning. George took out a personal loan for $15,000 at 9.5% interest. That should get him through his tax crisis. He would have to pay $_____ in interest in a year.

$ _____ loan

x _____% interest
_____

$ _____ interest in year

- -

On his way home from the office, George stopped to get gas. He bought 10.5 gallons of gas. The excise tax was 16.2 extra cents per gallon. So George was taxed another $_____. (Round off to the nearest cent.)

_____ gallons

x _____¢ excise tax
_____

_____¢ tax = $_____

- -

A group of children was waiting outside George's house. They were yelling, "You haven't paid your school tax! You owe 0.7% of the $280,000 value of your home." George leaned back in his car and closed his eyes. That would be another $_____.

_____ value of house

x _____% for school tax
_____

$ _____ for school tax

- -

George felt like having a good dinner. He went to his favorite restaurant. The dinner bill was $250. That must be a mistake! A 15% tip alone would be $_____.

$ _____ dinner bill

x _____% of bill for tip
_____

$ _____ amount of tip

Suddenly, George was in bed in his apartment. The alarm had just gone off. What a terrible nightmare he had!

Christmas in August

Alex Dugan laughs when his wife Katy does her Christmas shopping at the summer sales. He doesn't laugh in December. Then he's out at the mall fighting with other holiday shoppers.

Katy doesn't take a calculator, but she's a pro when it comes to estimating sale prices. First, she rounds the original price to the nearest dollar. Then she uses various methods to find the savings and final price.

Last year, she got a train that cost $29.95 for her nephew. At the toy store it was 20% off. Katy figured to herself, "$29.95 can be rounded to $30. It's easier to figure 10% of that, which is $3, and double it to get 20%, which is $6. The train will cost about $30 minus $6, which is $_____."

At the toy store, Katy bought two sets of doll furniture for her daughter. The kitchen set was $11.95, and the living room set was $15.99. Katy figured the kitchen set cost about $_____ and the living room set cost about $_____. That was a total of $_____. There was a 10% discount on doll furniture. The total price would be about $_____ for both sets.

Christie's sells brand-name clothing at reduced prices. Here Katy selected a pretty silk blouse for her mother that cost $19.95, nearly $_____. For her older daughter, Katy got a wool dress for $34.95, close to $_____. Together, the blouse and the dress would cost about $_____. The additional 10% special discount saved Katy about $_____, so the gifts would cost about $_____. The 5% sales tax (half of 10% of the total price) added about $_____. The final price would be about $_____.

Next, Katy went to Abe's, a discount center for household items. She found a set of non-stick pans for her best friend Ellen. They were $39.95, close to $_____. For her brother Donald she selected an electric screw driver at $24.95, close to $_____. Together the two gifts would cost about $_____. The store was offering an additional 15% off, so Katy paid about $_____ for the gifts. The 5% sales tax came to $_____.

Katy wanted to get an exercise bike for the whole family. She found a good one on sale. The usual price was $180, but there was a 33⅓% discount during the sale. She only had to pay $_____ for the bike.

Alex asked Katy in September if she was finished with her Christmas shopping. She was almost done. The next weekend, she bought a $59.95 jacket for Alex that was on sale at a 20% discount. The jacket had originally cost close to $_____. To figure the discount, Katy multiplied 10% of the price by 2. The discount was $_____. The sale price of the jacket was about $_____.

She also bought Alex a tie for $14.95, close to $_____. The total for the jacket and the tie would be about $_____. The 5% sales tax on that is about $_____. Katy gave the cashier $70 and expected about $_____ in change.

Now Katy had no more shopping to do. She could really enjoy the holiday season.

Percent Made, Percent Paid

T. S. Ryan:

I have a diner. To attract new customers, I put some video games in the back room. Last week, customers spent a total of $1,268 playing the games. I get 40% of that. Last week I made $_____ from the video games. It's a nice deal.

Buck Emery:

I'm a sales representative. Like most sales reps, I get a percentage of what I sell. Lumber is my product. I get a 12% commission on the lumber that I sell. Last week I sold $7,250 worth of wood. I made $_____.

Emma Jean Jordon:

Have you ever been in Sol's Eatery? I'm a waitress there. There are 5 of us. We pool our tips and divide them equally at the end of the shift. We each get _____% of the tips. Yesterday we had $125.50 in the pool. That wasn't bad. Each of us got $_____.

Master Sergeant Amos Greely:

I joined the Army 35 years ago. I'm going to retire next year. I'm earning $30,200 a year now. I'll get $24,160 a year in retirement. So, while I enjoy my free time, the army will pay me _____% of my salary.

Jemma Jones:

I used an employment agency to find a job. I had to pay the agency 50% of my first month's wages. I earn $1,190 a month, so I paid the agency $_____.

Mamie Griswold:

I manage a neighborhood grocery store. I pay $1,200
a month to rent the space. A couple of farmers I know
in Troyville wanted to sell fresh fruit and vegetables in
my store. I offered them the use of 25% of the space if they
paid 25% of the rent. They pay $_____ toward the rent
each month.

David Charles:

My friend Bruce and I rent an apartment for $4,800 a year.
Along with the first month's rent, we had to pay a security
deposit. The security deposit was 10% of a year's rent.
It came to $_____.

Max Gordon:

I sold a piece of property that I owned for $24,000. The
real estate company that arranged the deal charged me
a commission of $1,440. That was _____% of the sale
price. The saleswoman got 40% of the commission, which
was $_____. The company got the other 60%, $_____.

Maria Carlos:

My new stove cost $594. I will pay for it over 18 months.
The interest for that time will add 14% to the cost of
the stove. The interest will be $_____. Altogether,
my new stove will cost me $_____.

Art Johnson:

I bought my family a new television set for $240.
Including the interest on my loan, the total cost was $270.
The interest added _____% to the price of the set.

City Events Cashier

I work at the city office that organizes city-wide events. Before an event, I work at the main box office. On the day of an event, I'm at the city arena, the auditorium, or the ballpark. I sell tickets and take in the cash. You could call me the "city events cashier."

Every year, the city holds a marathon and track meet. Both events benefit the children's hospital. The track meet is in the arena. It holds 9,500 people. This year, we sold 7,125 tickets in advance. That's _____% of the tickets. The other _____% were bought on the day of the meet.

The marathon is run through city streets. This year, 1,095 runners entered the race. Only 657 runners finished the race. That's _____% of those who entered. Another 20%, _____ runners, came within a mile of finishing. A lot of money was raised for the children's hospital.

The auditorium seats 1,500 people. At $5.50 a ticket, we make $8,250 if all tickets are sold. For the last band concert, we sold $6,600 worth of tickets before the day of the concert. That's _____% of the tickets. For next week's concert, we've only sold 15% of the tickets, for a total so far of $_____.

The baseball park bleachers hold 6,500 people. We sold 4,225 tickets for the final game of the season. That's _____% of the seats. Each game, we give away 325 tickets to the schools for kids who can't afford to buy them. So, _____% of our seating goes to those kids.

The university in town has a great basketball team. The 9,500 seats in the arena are always sold out for their games. About 3,800 tickets are reserved for students. So, _____% of the spectators are students. Reporters for TV, radio, and newspapers get 1% of the seats. That means _____ seats are reserved for them.

Every year, the circus comes to town for five days. Each nightly performance lasts 2 hours. The clowns appear for 18 minutes each night. That's _____% of the time. Forty-five percent (45%) of the show includes animals. That means that animals are on for _____ minutes each night.

I get to see many events for free, and sometimes I meet famous people. Once, Kenny Rogers was the grand marshal of our Fourth of July parade. There are about 158,000 people in our town. We estimated that 142,200 of them lined the streets to see Kenny. That's _____% of the town!

I shook his hand when he gave his concert at the auditorium. It was full! We sold all 1,500 tickets with no trouble. We could have sold another 1,000. That would have been _____% more.
(Round off to the nearest whole number.)

Last year, a company came to the auditorium to test a new weight-loss product. At the opening event, 483 people signed up. A month later, those people returned. Hiram Uncan weighed 320 pounds at the start of the month. He lost 40 pounds, which was _____% of his original weight. Maggie Turnbull had weighed 200 pounds. She lost 22 pounds, _____% of her original weight.

As you can see, many events go on in this city.

Basketball Scores

Stop the presses! Before you read about your favorite basketball team or player, learn how the experts analyze the numbers. They compare statistics. There are many different statistics to look at. Be an expert!

Winning Percentage:

When you see a team's winning percentage in the sports pages, it means the percentage of their games they have won. To calculate a basketball team's winning percentage, divide the number of games won by the number of games played. Then multiply that number by 100 to make a percent. In the first half of the season, the Hawks played 40 games and won 34 of them. They won _____% of their games.

By the end of the season, the Hawks had played 80 games and won 62 of them. Their winning percentage was _____% for the season.
(Round off to the nearest whole number.)

Field Goal Percentage:

Field goal percentage is the percentage of baskets a player makes out of total shots tried. To calculate field goal percentage, divide the number of baskets made by the number of baskets attempted. Then multiply that number by 100 to make a percentage. If Pete made 130 attempts and he made 70 baskets, his field goal percentage would be _____%. (Round off to the nearest whole number.)

At the end of the season, Pete had made 332 attempts and made 144 baskets, or goals. His field goal percentage was now _____%. (Round off to the nearest whole number.)

John Havlicek, who played for the Boston Celtics, attempted 23,900 field goals during his playing career. He made 10,513 goals, so his field goal percentage was _____%. (Round off to the nearest whole number.)

Wilt Chamberlain attempted 23,497 field goals during his basketball career. He made 12,681 field goals. His field goal percentage was _____%.
(Round off to the nearest whole number.)

Free Throw Percentage:
A free throw is the shot players take after they're fouled. No one is allowed to interfere with this shot, and it is worth one point. To calculate free throw percentage, divide the number of free throws made by the number attempted. If Bonnie had 25 attempts and made 15 free throws, her free throw percentage would be _____%.

Everett gets fouled a lot. In one season, he attempted 72 free throws and made 60. His free throw percentage was _____%. (Round off to the nearest whole number.)

Wilt Chamberlain attempted 11,862 free throws during his career. He made 6,057, so his free throw percentage was _____%. (Round off to the nearest whole number.)

Oscar Robertson attempted 9,185 free throws and made 7,694 of them. His free throw percentage was _____%.
(Round off to the nearest whole number.)

Bike or Hike Shop

Pedro Gomez:
At the Bike or Hike Shop, Mr. Kane sells new and used bikes, and fixes broken ones. I put my old bike in Mr. Kane's shop to sell. Mr. Kane fixed it up and got $85 for it. He took a 35% commission which was $_____.

Dennis King:
My wife and I bought bikes last year. She chose a green one for $145 and I picked out a red one for $178. We had to pay 4.5% sales tax. We paid $_____ for the two bikes, including the tax. (Round off to the nearest cent.)

Mrs. Reed:
When my son Jamie turned six, I thought it was time that he had a two-wheeled bike. At the Bike or Hike Shop, Jamie and I found the perfect dark blue bike. The bike cost $68.60 plus 4.5% sales tax. The total cost was $_____.
(Round off to the nearest cent.)

Toby Smith:
My new bike cost $164 at the Bike or Hike Shop. With the 4.5% sales tax, the bike cost me $_____. I put down $42.58. Now I owed $_____ for the bike. I paid 10% each week, which came to $_____ a month. It took me _____ months to pay off the bike.

Mr. Kane:
I bring in about $35,000 a year from the Bike or Hike Shop. Almost 65% is made on repairs, parts, and selling used bikes. The rest, about $_____, is made by selling new bikes.

ANSWERS: Self-Check

FRACTIONS

The Butcher (p. 5)

$5\frac{2}{3}$ pounds, roast

6 pounds, two chickens

$2\frac{7}{8}$ pounds, meat

$\frac{1}{4}$ pound added

$2\frac{4}{5}$ pounds, both steaks

$8\frac{1}{2}$ pounds, meat

$4\frac{1}{4}$ pounds, ground beef

Number One (p. 7)

$\frac{15}{16}$, Hoffman

$\frac{8}{9}$, Krantz

$1\frac{1}{12}$, Smith; *more than*; *did not* accept

$\frac{14}{15}$, Page; *less* than; *was* acceptable

$\frac{9}{10}$, O'Brien

$1\frac{1}{10}$, Dean; *more* than, *did not* accept

$\frac{23}{24}$, Norris

$\frac{17}{18}$, Perdue

Jim Norris came closest.

Union Dues (p. 9)

$\frac{5}{6}$ want raise; $\frac{1}{6}$ want more benefits

$\frac{7}{10}$ with opinion; $\frac{3}{10}$, no opinion

$\frac{1}{20}$ of working year

$\frac{7}{8}$ answered question;
$\frac{1}{8}$ didn't answer question

$\frac{17}{24}$ had opinion; $\frac{7}{24}$ no opinion

$\frac{2}{3}$ wanted 6 or 8 weeks;
$\frac{1}{3}$ wanted 3 months

Odd Jobs (p. 11)

$11\frac{1}{6}$ hours' difference

$2\frac{7}{8}$ inches of rain

$4\frac{1}{12}$ pints more

$5\frac{1}{12}$ hours, all three

$3\frac{5}{18}$ hours more

$7\frac{1}{4}$ feet wider; $5\frac{5}{9}$ feet deeper, day two

$1\frac{1}{8}$ hours longer

Washington, D.C. (p. 13)

$\frac{9}{11}$, Washington Monument

$\frac{1}{4}$ of day on tour

$\frac{1}{3}$ of the names

180 minutes in museum;
$\frac{1}{6}$ studying airplane

20 to baseball game; $\frac{5}{9}$ of members

72 hours in three days; $\frac{5}{12}$ on feet

Starting a Career (p. 15)

$\frac{2}{3}$ of her life

$\frac{1}{4}$ of a year

$\frac{5}{9}$ of the pregnant women

$\frac{6}{11}$ of all the pregnant women

$\frac{1}{8}$, class; $\frac{1}{6}$, babies; 12, costs

$\frac{1}{5}$ came by van

$\frac{1}{30}$ had real emergencies

$\frac{1}{3}$ of cost, Heidi to pay

$\frac{2}{5}$ of old hours

Speak Out (p. 17)

24 enrolled before first meeting

14 took class for their jobs

21 students

$4\frac{1}{2}$ hours a week, John practiced

$7\frac{1}{2}$ hours a week, Brigitte worked

5 minutes

16 talked about an event

6 minutes on main idea

$\frac{1}{4}$ of the 32 topics listed

$\frac{1}{3}$ chose own topics

was not long enough

14th-Street Firehouse (p. 19)

$\frac{1}{2}$ force off duty

56 hours, calls and other duties

$\frac{5}{12}$ out of 84 hours

4 hours on emergency calls

¼ of all fire fighters

$180,000

$2,500 each month

5¼ hours talking

180 hours for toy repair

The Addition (p. 21)

370 square feet

$1,030 for materials

$1,587, salary and equipment

$1,071 remaining;
   $1,785, total paid plumber

60 rolls of insulation

$925 for tiles

2⅚ long

10 shelves

$4,275, total; $5,700, we made

$68,400 in a year

The Home Aide (p. 23)

2 hours and 5 minutes, yard work

1 hour and 40 minutes, rest of house

3⁷⁄₁₂ hours out

1⅕ hours for cleaning

4 hours and 10 minutes worked

6:05 ready to leave

45 minutes reading

15¾ miles travels

DECIMALS

Olympic Meet (p. 25)

.32 seconds faster

.53 seconds slower

37.83 seconds, team's total time

2.01 seconds faster than Burke's

6.6 seconds faster, Paine

7.11 seconds slower than Burger's

4 minutes, 8.76 seconds, 1980 time

26.1 seconds faster than '60 team

The Produce Market (p. 27)

$1 for 2 pounds; $1.25 for 2.5 pounds

$1.20 for 1 pint; $4.80 for 4 pints

bananas: 3 pounds, 90¢; .5 pounds, 15¢;
   about $1.05 total

eating apples: about 70¢ pound;
   about 77¢ total

baking apples: nearly 60¢ pound;
   3 pounds, $1.80; .25 pounds, 15¢;
   about $1.95 total

green beans: about 40¢ pound;
   almost 3 pounds; about $1.20 total

spinach: almost $1.40; .5 pounds, 70¢;
   about $2.10 total

lettuce: about $1

watercress: about $1 pound;
   .25 pounds, 25¢; about $1.25 total

Mick the Mechanic (p. 29)

.8 miles shorter

2.9 more miles per gallon

58.5 miles per hour

88.55 kilometers per hour

406.5 miles today

219.1 miles traveled

30 miles on every gallon; 13.9 gallons

Eric's car

$123.51, average bill

Baseball Scores (p. 31)

.563, Bears' winning average

.467, Eagles' winning average

.350, Joe's batting average

.247, average for season

.367, Cobb's lifetime average

.305, Aaron's lifetime average

2.25, Evan's ERA

2.03, ERA later in season

Hubbell's won-lost percentage, 73%

Guidry's won-lost percentage, 89%

PERCENTS

Family Budget (p. 33)

$750, rent

$500, regular expenses

$475, car and utilities

$125, clothing and shoes

$150, medical bills

$900, insurance

$250 saved a month; 1.8 months

$19,080, new salary

Taxes, Taxes, Taxes (p. 35)

$26,253, federal taxes

$50.76, sales tax

$4,375.50, state income tax

$1,400, property tax

$1,425, interest in one year

170¢ = $1.70 excise tax

$1,960, school tax

$37.50 amount of tip

Christmas in August (p. 37)

about $24, train

about $12; $16; $28; $25.20, both sets

nearly $20; $35; $55; $5.50; $49.50;
$2.48; about $52 ($51.98) final price

close to $40; $25; $65; $55.25; $2.76, tax

$120 for bike

close to $60; $12; $48

$15; $63; $3.15;
about $4 ($3.85) in change

Percent Made, Percent Paid (p. 39)

$507.20 from video games

$870 made

20% of tips; $25.10 each

80% of salary

$595 paid agency

$300 toward rent

$480, security deposit

6% of sales price; $576, saleswoman;
$864, company

$83.16, interest; $677.16 altogether

12.5% added to price

City Events Cashier (p. 41)

75% of tickets; 25% on day

60% finished; 219 runners

80% of tickets; $1,237.50 so far

65% of seats; 5% to kids

40% students; 95 seats reserved

15% of time; 54 minutes each night

90% of town

67% more

12.5% of his weight; 11% of her weight

Basketball Scores (p. 43)

85% of games, Hawks won

78%, winning percentage

54%, Pete, field goal percentage

43% at end of season

44%, Havlicek, field goal percentage

54%, Chamberlain, field goal percentage

60%, Bonnie, free throw percentage

83%, Everett, free throw percentage

51%, Chamberlain

84%, Robertson

Bike or Hike Shop (p. 45)

$29.75 commission

$337.54 for two bikes

$71.69, total cost

$171.38, bike; $128.80, owed;
$51.52 a month; 2½ months to pay

$12,250 selling new bikes